Jesus Walks on Water

and other Bible Stories

Retold by Vic Parker

Miles
Kelly

First published in 2011 by Miles Kelly Publishing Ltd
Harding's Barn, Bardfield End Green, Thaxted, Essex, CM6 3PX, UK

2 4 6 8 10 9 7 5 3 1

EDITORIAL DIRECTOR *Belinda Gallagher*
ART DIRECTOR *Jo Cowan*
EDITOR *Carly Blake*
DESIGNERS *Michelle Cannatella, Joe Jones*
JUNIOR DESIGNER *Kayleigh Allen*
COVER DESIGNER *Joe Jones*
CONSULTANT *Janet Dyson*
PRODUCTION MANAGER *Elizabeth Collins*
REPROGRAPHICS *Stephan Davis, Ian Paulyn*

ISBN 978-1-84810-401-3

Printed in China

British Library Cataloguing-in-Publication Data
A catalogue record for this book is available from the British Library

ACKNOWLEDGEMENTS
The publishers would like to thank the following artists
who have contributed to this book:

The Bright Agency Katriona Chapman, Dan Crisp,
Giuliano Ferri (inc. cover), Mélanie Florian

Advocate Art Alida Massari

*The publishers would like to thank Robert Willoughby and
the London School of Theology for their help in compiling this book.*

Made with paper from a sustainable forest

www.mileskelly.net   info@mileskelly.net

www.factsforprojects.com

Self-publish your
children's book

buddingpress.co.uk

Contents

Jesus Walks on Water

It had been a long day at the Sea of Galilee. Jesus told his weary disciples to head for home without Him while He sent away the thousands of people who had gathered.

"It's going to take a little while for me to convince everyone to leave," Jesus said to His friends with a sigh. "You start off without me. I want to spend some time praying on my own. I'll catch up with you later."

"But how will you follow us?" The disciples protested, clambering into their little boats.

"Don't worry, I'll be fine," Jesus reassured, waving them off.

As the men sailed away, Jesus turned back to the crowds and told them it was time to go home too. No one wanted to leave Him, but eventually they began to wander away in groups.

At last, Jesus was able to leave unnoticed and went a little way up a hillside. Finally, He had some peace and quiet and could pray alone. He stayed for quite a while, deep in thought, talking to God.

Meanwhile out on the Sea of Galilee, the disciples were in trouble. The wind had grown stronger, stirring up strong currents in the water and battering the little boats. The alarmed men had rolled up the sails and tried to row to shore, but despite straining at the oars with all their might, the boats were being blown off course, right into dangerous open waters.

Hours passed and as the night grew darker, the wind grew wilder and the waves grew higher. The disciples realized they were lost at sea and they were terrified.

As they sat huddled in their boats, desperately waiting for the light of dawn, they saw a white glow in the darkness. It came closer and grew bigger, turning into the shape of a man.

"A ghost!" they cried, even more frightened than before. Then a voice came floating towards them on the wind.

"Don't be afraid. It's me, Jesus."

The disciples were confused. Was it really their friend and master? Or was a demon trying to trick them?

Peter spoke up bravely. "If it's really you, Lord," he shouted back, "tell me to walk to you across the waves."

"Yes, come then," Jesus called.

Peter stood up, cautiously moved to the edge of the rocking boat and took a deep breath. The other disciples could hardly believe their eyes as Peter stepped out.

Far from sinking into the churning waters, their friend strode from wave to wave, over the swirling sea, towards Jesus.

Peter kept his eyes fixed on Jesus, not daring to look down. But when he was within a couple of steps of Jesus, his curiosity got the better of him and he glanced down. The moment he saw the frothing foam beneath his feet, his courage deserted him and he plunged down into the dark, cold waters. "Help me, Jesus!" Peter screamed in a panic. "I'm sinking!"

Jesus reached out and grabbed Peter's hand, heaving him up. "Don't doubt me," He said. "Have more faith." Jesus guided his friend back to the boats and suddenly the wind died down and the waves calmed.

The disciples had watched everything in

amazement. "You really are the Son of God," they said, falling in awe at Jesus' feet.

Matthew chapter 14; Mark chapter 6; John chapter 6

A Story of Forgiveness

Jesus told a story about a farmer who had two sons. The farmer was teaching his sons all about farming so that when he passed away, they could take over. However one day, the younger son approached his father with an idea.

"I've been thinking, father," he said nervously. "I'm grown up and it's time I saw a bit of the world. It would help if I could have my share of the farm now in cash."

The farmer loved his sons dearly and he didn't even have to think about the decision. He counted hundreds of silver coins into bags and handed them to the excited lad.

"Thank you, father," he said, packing his bags to set off. "You won't regret it."

And the farmer watched with tears in his eyes as his younger son left home.

For a while the farmer's son had a wonderful time. He lived like a prince, visiting the finest cities, eating out every night and going to parties. He was surrounded by people who wanted to be his friend, but the problem was they helped him

spend all his money.

When the silver was gone, his friends vanished too. The young man found himself alone and far from home, without even a few pennies to buy a loaf of bread. To make matters worse, a dreadful drought swept through the land, causing a terrible famine. The farmer's son couldn't even beg for food because no one had enough for themselves. Luckily, he found a job as a pig-keeper. But the wages were pitiful. He had hardly enough money left to buy food after paying his rent. Some days he was so hungry he nearly ate the food for the pigs!

One day, he decided enough was enough. "I want to go home," he groaned. "I'll beg my father for his forgiveness for being such an idiot. He's bound to be furious, but maybe if I grovel, he'll let me stay and work as one of his farm labourers." The miserable, ragged young man arrived home and couldn't believe how overjoyed his father was to see him. "I've worried about you and missed you every day, son," the farmer cried, hugging and kissing him.

The ashamed son sobbed as he told his father what had happened.

"Never mind," the farmer said, to his son's utter astonishment. "You're back

home now and we're together again. That's all that matters."

Later, the farmer's elder son came home from a hard day's work in the fields to find a party in full swing. The neighbours had been invited over to celebrate his son's return, and a feast had been prepared. There was music, dancing and the people were drinking wine.

"Whatever's going on here?" he gasped, and one of the servants explained what had happened.

The farmer swung his elder son round in a jig. "Rejoice!" he cried. "Your little brother has finally come back home!"

"What do you mean, 'rejoice'?" the elder son spat, completely furious. "I've stayed with you all these years, working my fingers to the bone, and you've never given me so much as a thank you – let alone thrown me a party! Then HE turns up, having wasted most of your fortune, and you're celebrating how wonderful he is!"

"You have no idea how much your faithfulness means to me," the farmer said to his elder son, drawing him close in a hug. "Everything I have, I give to you. But today is a day to be glad, for your brother was lost and gone forever, but he has come home."

Luke chapter 15

The Pharisee and the Tax Collector

The Pharisees were Jews who had been brought up to live according to strict religious rules. They believed that their ways of living were the right ways – the only ways – and everyone who didn't follow their rules were not as good as them.

However, Jesus often warned the Pharisees that they were committing all sorts of sins without realizing it. One was the sin of looking down on others, and He told this story to try to make the Pharisees think about it.

"Two men went into the temple to pray. One was a Pharisee," the Pharisees in the crowd of listeners all smiled smugly, "and one was a tax collector," people booed and hissed at the thought of the traitors who worked for the Romans. "The Pharisee strode straight into the middle of the temple," Jesus continued, "in full view of the people around. He lifted his arms, raised his eyes to the heavens and prayed in a loud, confident voice so that everyone could clearly hear him. 'Thank you, O God,' he said, 'for making me better than common sinners. Thank you for not making me a liar or a cheat like most people. Thank you for giving me the strength to fast twice a week and the generosity to give part of everything I earn to charity. Thank you for not making me like that greedy tax collector over there.'

"The tax collector was lurking behind a pillar in the shadows, trying his best not to be noticed by anyone. He knelt and bowed his head low, whispering, 'Lord, I am a sinner. I ask for forgiveness, even though I am not worthy of your mercy.'

"Now," finished Jesus, "That day it was the tax collector who went home with God's blessing. For those who set

themselves up high will one day fall, and those who think of themselves as lowly will one day be raised up."

Of course the Pharisees didn't like that particular story one little bit.

Luke chapter 18

Jesus and the Children

The twelve disciples were travelling with Jesus along a road one day. They began to fall behind, squabbling among themselves. Their argument was about which of them would be the greatest in the Kingdom of Heaven. They thought that Jesus couldn't hear them, but He did. They were saying things like, "Well, I should be the greatest because I'm Jesus' oldest friend…" And, "I should be the greatest because I've performed the most miracles…" And, "No, I'm sure I'll be the greatest because I pray the most often."

Jesus didn't stop them, He just listened to every word. But later on when they had reached their destination and sat down to rest, He asked, "So what were you all talking about on the road then?"

The disciples felt embarrassed to think that Jesus had heard them trying to outdo each other. No one admitted a thing, but Jesus knew all about what had gone on. "If you really want to be the greatest in God's eyes, you must put others before yourself," He told the red-faced men. Jesus reached out to a little girl who was passing by and drew her towards Him. "You must be like this child," He said. "You must have simple, honest values and take genuine delight in helping others. Never look down on children, for they are selfless and giving. They are among the greatest in Heaven."

However, it didn't take long for the disciples to forget what Jesus had told them. A few weeks later, Jesus had been preaching all day long when a group of people with young children approached, asking Him to bless them. Some of the children clung to their parents, while others were playful and pestered Jesus for attention.

Jesus' disciples were sure that this would be annoying for the weary preacher and they began to shoo the children away. But Jesus stopped His friends. "Let the children come to me," He instructed. "After all, the Kingdom of Heaven belongs to them." Jesus picked up the smallest child and let others scramble onto his lap, blessing them all. "Unless you are pure and wholehearted like these children," He warned His disciples once more, "you will never see God."

Matthew chapters 18, 19;
Mark chapters 9, 10;
Luke chapters 9, 18

Jesus the Good Shepherd

Jesus once said to a crowd that had gathered to hear Him speak, "What would a shepherd do if wolves attacked the sheep in his flock? If he was a hired shepherd, doing his job only for the money, he wouldn't stay and fight off the wolves. He would run away and save himself, leaving the sheep to be eaten.

"I am not like that shepherd, I am the good shepherd. I will look after my sheep even if it means I have to die for them. I have flocks in other places too, which I need to gather so I can look after all my animals together. My sheep know my voice, they will listen to me and follow me anywhere. It's because I will give up my life for my sheep willingly – for love, not any other reward – that God loves me and will give me my life back again."

Many of Jesus' listeners were bemused by these words. "He must be mad," some of them mumbled. "Do you think it's demons inside Him that are talking?"

But others knew that Jesus was trying to get them to understand something important. "Of course He's not mad!" they insisted, even though they weren't sure what Jesus meant. "How could someone possessed by demons miraculously heal people?"

What Jesus wanted everyone to know was that He genuinely cared for them. Not just for Jewish people, but for people everywhere who wanted to follow God. He was also warning that He was ready to die for everybody, if that is what He had to do. Jesus was explaining that it is only by loving everyone and willingly helping other people in this world, that God will reward us with new life in the next.

John chapter 10

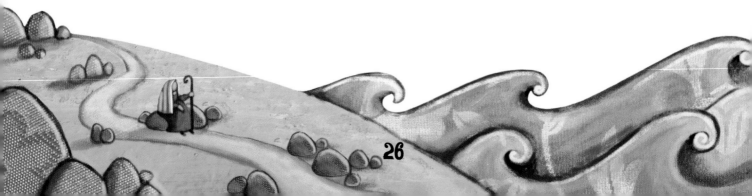

Bartimaeus, the Blind Beggar

Bartimaeus had been a blind beggar in Jericho for as long as anyone could remember. No one knew how old he was, probably not even Bartimaeus himself, but everyone knew who he was. He could always be found sitting in the same spot by the roadside. His begging bowl set on the ground in front of him, and lifting his poor, dull eyes hopefully to each passer-by.

One day Bartimaeus became aware of quite a fuss building around him. "What's going on?" he asked. "Why are there so many people around?"

"Jesus of Nazareth is coming this way," someone replied.

At once, Bartimaeus' heart began to beat faster. He had heard many stories about the great preacher – how He had given the gift of sight to hundreds of blind people just like him. Jesus had healed paralyzed people, cured the lame, made the sick well again. It was rumoured that Jesus had even brought people back from the dead.

As the crowds bustled around the beggar, he stumbled to his feet and added his voice to theirs. "Jesus! Have pity on me!" he shouted as loud as he could.

"Be quiet, Bartimaeus! Shut up!"came voices from around him. "Jesus is coming and we want to hear what He is saying."

But that just encouraged old Bartimaeus to shout even louder. "Jesus of Nazareth! Help me!" he bellowed, with a strength he didn't know he had. "I'm over here. Please take pity on me!"

Suddenly, the commotion all around him fell silent and he felt a hand on his shoulder.

"My friend, I'm here," came a soft voice. "How would you like me to help you?"

Trembling, Bartimaeus gasped, "Oh Lord, please let me see."

The ragged man felt gentle fingertips touch his eyelids. Then all at once the darkness before him began to lighten and

brighten until he could make out blurs…
then shapes and colours… He could see!
The world was unimaginably beautiful, and
Bartimaeus looked at Jesus'
smiling face.

"Your faith has made
you well," Jesus said, and
Bartimaeus followed Him,
dancing in celebration
along the road.

Matthew chapter 20; Mark chapter 10;
Luke chapter 18

The Parable of the Lost Coins

Despite everything Jesus had told His followers, there were many people who thought that He was going to establish God's Kingdom by forming an army and marching against the Romans. Jesus knew that He wasn't going to win any earthly revolution. In fact, He was going to be arrested, put on trial and then executed.

The Kingdom of Heaven would come at the end of the world, after Judgement Day, and only God knew when that would be. So Jesus told a parable that he hoped would help people make the most of everything God had given them, while they were waiting.

"There was once a prince who had to travel far away to lay claim to a kingdom that was rightfully his," Jesus began. "Before he went, he called his three most trusted servants and asked them to look after his property while he was away. To the first servant he gave five bags of gold. To the second servant he gave two bags and to the third servant he gave one bag. 'Use my money wisely and well,' he bade them.

"The prince left and years passed. Eventually he returned, now a great king. 'What did you do with my gold,' he asked his servants.

"The first servant traded with his five bags of gold and earned five more. The king was delighted and made him governor of ten of his new cities.

"The second servant had saved his two bags of gold in a bank, where it had doubled with interest making four bags. The king was pleased and made him governor of five new cities.

"The last servant had hidden his bag of gold in the ground. 'You mean to say you did nothing with my gift?' the king roared furiously. 'You made no use of it at all?' He turned to his guards. 'Take this man's gold and then throw him out,' he commanded. 'Give the gold to the servant who already has ten bags. For those who try hard will be rewarded, while those who do not will lose what little they have.'

Matthew chapter 25; Luke chapter 19

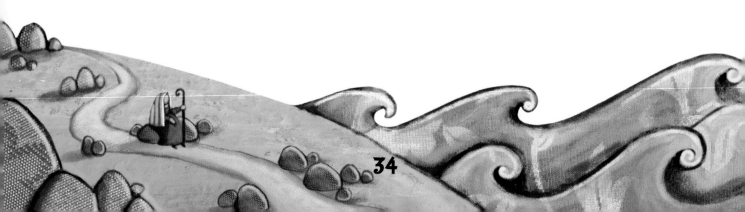

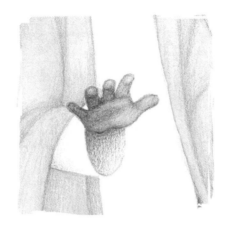

Jesus Warns of the Future

There came a rare moment when Jesus found Himself alone with His disciples, walking along a road. He took the opportunity to talk with them. "I sometimes call myself 'the Son of Man'," He began. "What do you think I mean by that?"

"Some people believe you are John the Baptist," one disciple shrugged.

"Or the prophet Elijah come back from the dead," another suggested.

"Or a new, greater prophet," a third said.

"But who do you think I am?" He asked.

"I think you are the Messiah, the Son of the Living God," Peter announced firmly.

"Then God has blessed you," Jesus said to Peter. "Your name means 'rock', and you are the rock on which I will build my church. I will give you the keys to Heaven, and whatever rules you set on Earth will also stand in Heaven."

Jesus turned to everyone and said gravely, "I must warn you all that things are soon going to get very difficult. The time is drawing near when I must go to Jerusalem. I will go through much suffering," Jesus gave a sigh. "And eventually I will be put to death." The disciples gasped, but Jesus held up his hands to silence them. "However, three days later, I will come back to life." The disciples were amazed.

"Are you ready to follow me into hardship and sorrow – even to die for me?" Jesus asked His friends. "If you are, I cannot grant you a reward in this world, but I can promise you joy in the next."

Jesus' friends walked on with heavy, but determined, hearts.

Matthew chapter 16; Mark chapter 8; Luke chapter 9

Jesus Shows Himself in Glory

One week had passed since Jesus told His disciples that He was the Messiah and warned them of the troubles to come. Now He asked Peter, James and John to go with Him up a hillside a little way to a quiet place where they could pray away from everyone else.

The four men were soon deep in prayer,

unaware of anything else around them. But suddenly something made Peter, James and John stop talking to God and turn to look at Jesus. They were shocked to see their kneeling friend so transfixed in prayer. His body looked still and lifeless like a statue, as if His spirit had left it. Jesus' face began to glow brighter and brighter, and His clothes glared whiter and whiter, until He was surrounded by a blaze of glory. It hurt their eyes to look at Him, so they shielded them with their hands.

Two other gleaming figures appeared whom they recognized as the great prophets, Moses and Elijah. They listened as Jesus discussed with them what He would have to face in Jerusalem, including His own death.

Then suddenly a towering black cloud surged overhead. "This is my Son, the Chosen One. Listen to Him!" boomed a mighty voice. The disciples were terrified.

When they looked up again, everything had returned to normal. "Don't tell anyone what you have seen," Jesus commanded, "until I have died and risen from the dead."

Matthew chapter 17; Mark chapter 9; Luke chapter 9